# Plane Geometry

### Tests / Quizzes

*A Beka Book*® Pensacola, FL 32523-9100
an affiliate of PENSACOLA CHRISTIAN COLLEGE®

## Correlated Materials

**Student Materials**
*Plane Geometry*
Test / Quiz Book
**Teacher Materials**
Teacher Edition
Solution Key
Test / Quiz Key

*Plane Geometry*

*Editors:* R. McLaughlin, M. Ashworth, E. Collins

Photos: front cover, title page–iStockphoto, stock.xchng; back cover–Photodisc/ Fotosearch.

Copyright © mmvi, mcmlxxxviii  Pensacola Christian College
All rights reserved.  Printed in U.S.A.  2008  C08

Name _____     Date _____     Score _____

_____

**CIRCLE:** Write the special name for each of the following parts.

_____     **1.** *AC*

_____     **2.** *O*

_____     **3.** *ED*

_____     **4.** *OB*

_____     **5.** arc *ABC*

**COMPLETION:** Write the correct answer in the blank at the left.

_____     **6.** The distance around a circle is the __?__ .

_____     **7.** All radii of a circle are __?__ .

_____     **8.** Two geometric figures that have the same *shape* and *size* are __?__ .

_____     **9.** If $\triangle ABC \cong \triangle DEF$, then *BC* corresponds to __?__ .

_____     **10.** If $\triangle ABC \cong \triangle DEF$, then $\angle BCA$ corresponds to $\angle$ __?__ .

Name _____ Date _____ Score _____

**QUIZ 6**

**CONSTRUCTIONS:** Construct each figure according to the given description.

1. Construct the perpendicular bisector of *AB*.

2. Construct an angle at *P* equal to angle *ABC*.

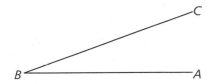

3. Construct a perpendicular to *CD* at *P*.

Name _____  Date _____  Score _____

**CONSTRUCTIONS:** Construct each figure according to the given description.

1. Construct a triangle with the three sides given below.

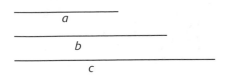

2. Construct a perpendicular to *AB* from *P.*

P •

A _____ B

Name _____ Date _____ Score _____

**COMPLETION:** Write the correct answer in the blank at the left.

_____  1. The shortest line between two points is ___?___ .

_____  2. Two points determine ___?___ .

_____  3. Geometric statements accepted as true without proof are called ___?___ .

_____  4. The number of perpendiculars that can be drawn to a line at a given point in the line is ___?___ .

_____  5. Complements of the same angle, or equal angles, are ___?___ .

_____  6. The sum of all the angles about a point on one side of a straight line is ___?___ .

_____  7. All right angles are ___?___ .

_____  8. The sum of any two sides of a triangle is (equal to, greater than, less than) the third side. *(Choose the correct comparison.)*

_____  9. If equals are subtracted from equals, the ___?___ are equal.

_____ 10. The whole is equal to ___?___ .

Name _____ Date _____ Score _____

# QUIZ 9

**MULTIPLE CHOICE:** Write the correct answer.

_____ 1. The definitions, axioms, theorems, etc. used to support each statement in a formal two-column proof are called the __?__ .
 **a.** given          **c.** analysis
 **b.** reasons

_____ 2. A statement of beginning facts about lines, angles, figures, etc. to be used in a proof is known as the __?__ .
 **a.** given                    **c.** analysis
 **b.** reasons

**COMPLETION:** Write the correct answer in the blank at the left.

_____ 3. A geometric statement that is not self-evident but proved by a chain of reasoning is a(n) __?__ .

_____ 4. A geometric statement that is easily deduced from a theorem is a(n) __?__ .

_____ 5. Before one can use C.P.C.T.E. in a proof, it must first be given or proved that __?__ .

**TRIANGLES:** Use the figure below to answer questions 6–10.

_____ 6. If *AB* = *DE*, *BC* = *EF*, and ∠*B* = ∠*E*, then what may be deduced, and (7) why?

_____ 7.

_____ 8. If *AC* ⊥ *BC*, *DF* ⊥ *EF*, *AC* = *DF*, and ∠*A* = ∠*D*, then what may be deduced, and (9) why?

_____ 9.

_____ 10. If *A* and *D* are right angles and *AC* = *DF*, then what other sides must be known to be equal in order to prove that the triangles are congruent by L.L.?

Name _____ Date _____ Score _____

**TEST 2** _____ *Plane Geometry*

**TRUE/FALSE:** Write *true* if the statement is always true; write *false* if it is not always true.

_____ 1. The whole is greater than the sum of all its parts.

_____ 2. All right angles are equal.

_____ 3. Two angles that are complementary to the same angle or equal angles are supplementary to each other.

_____ 4. A quantity may be substituted for its equal in any process.

_____ 5. Two straight lines can intersect in several points at one time.

_____ 6. If the sum of two adjacent angles is a straight angle, then they are complementary angles.

_____ 7. The sum of two sides of a triangle is less than the third side.

_____ 8. The sum of all the angles about a given point is a straight angle.

_____ 9. Two right triangles are congruent if the two legs of one triangle are equal respectively to the two legs of the other triangle.

_____ 10. An exterior angle of a triangle is greater than either opposite interior angle.

_____ 11. The eye is a valid means for testing the truth of a construction.

_____ 12. A diameter of a circle is also a chord.

(continued)

**MULTIPLE CHOICE:** Read each statement carefully, and decide which of the following terms is being described. Write the letter of the answer in the blank space.
(**a.** analysis) (**b.** axiom) (**c.** construction) (**d.** corollary) (**e.** postulate) (**f.** theorem)

_____ **13.** A geometric statement that is easily deduced from a theorem

_____ **14.** A pre-proof planning of how to complete a proof

_____ **15.** A geometric statement that is not self-evident but proven by a chain of reasoning

_____ **16.** A figure that satisfies given conditions and is drawn without instruments of measurement

_____ **17.** A geometric statement that is accepted without proof to be true

**COMPLETION:** Write the word(s) in the blank at the left that best completes the statement.

_____ **18.** A radius of a circle is equal to half the length of the __?__ .

_____ **19.** Added lines in a diagram used to aid in solving proofs are called __?__ lines.

_____ **20.** The arc that represents one quarter of a circle is a(n) __?__ .

_____ **21.** The sum of all the angles about a point on one side of a straight line is __?__ .

_____ **22.** The process of reasoning that establishes the truth of a theorem or the correctness of a construction is called a(n) __?__ .

_____ **23.** A line can be bisected by but one __?__ .

_____ **24.** Two geometric figures that have the same shape and size are __?__ .

_____ **25.** The shortest line that can be drawn between two points is __?__ .

_____ **26.** Any two straight lines intersect to form equal __?__ angles.

_____ **27.** The instrument used for drawing circles is the ___?___ .

_____ **28.** In two congruent figures, the equal parts are called ___?___ parts.

_____ **29.** If △*ABC* ≅ △*JKL*, the three pairs of equal sides are ___?___ .

_____ **30.** If △*CAB* ≅ △*FEG*, the three pairs of equal angles are ___?___ .

**AXIOMS:** From the list below, select the main axiom that justifies the stated conclusion from the conditions for each figure.  Axioms may be used once, more than once, or not at all.

    **a.** The whole is equal to the sum of all its parts.
    **b.** If equals are added to equals, the sums are equal.
    **c.** Quantities that are equal to the same quantity or equal
       quantities are equal to each other.
    **d.** If equals are subtracted from equals, the remainders are equal.
    **e.** Doubles of equals are equal.

_____ **31.** Given: *AB* = *DE*, *BC* = *EF*
         Prove: *AC* = *DF*

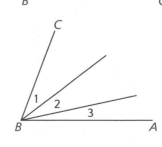

_____ **32.** Given: *AB* = *AC*, *DB* = *EC*
         Prove: *AD* = *AE*

_____ **33.** Given: ∠1, ∠2, ∠3
         Prove: ∠*ABC* = ∠1 + ∠2 + ∠3

_____ **34.** Given: *AB* = *AD*, *DC* = *AD*
         Prove: *AB* = *DC*

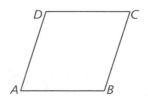

(continued)

**AXIOMS** (cont.)

    **a.** The whole is equal to the sum of all its parts.
    **b.** If equals are added to equals, the sums are equal.
    **c.** Quantities that are equal to the same quantity or equal quantities are equal to each other.
    **d.** If equals are subtracted from equals, the remainders are equal.
    **e.** Doubles of equals are equal.

_____ **35.** Given: $\angle BCF = \angle EDA$, $\angle ACF = \angle FDA$
             Prove: $\angle 1 = \angle 2$

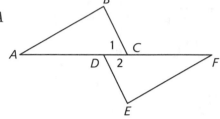

_____ **36.** Given: $AC = BC$, $BC = BA$
             Prove: $AC = BA$

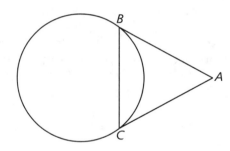

**CONSTRUCTIONS:** Construct each figure according to the given description.

**37.** Given: Line $XY$
    Required: To bisect $XY$

28

**38.** Given: Line *CD* and point *P* not
           on line *CD*
    Required: To construct a perpendicular
             from *CD* through point *P*

*P* •

C———————————————————————————D

**39.** Given: ∠*COD*
    Required: Bisect ∠*COD*

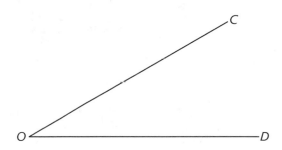

(continued)

**PROOF:** Fill in the steps to complete the proof.

**40.** Given: *AD* is a straight line, and *AE* = *DB*, *AC* = *DF*, ∠*A* = ∠*D*
Prove: ∠*C* = ∠*F*

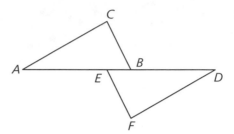

| **Proof: Statements** | **Reasons:** |
|---|---|
| 1. | 1. |
| 2. *AE* + *EB* = *DB* + *BE* | 2. |
| 3. | 3. The whole is equal to the sum of all its parts. |
| 4. | 4. |
| 5. | 5. |
| 6. | 6. |

Name _____  Date _____  Score _____

**COMPLETION:** Write the word(s) in the blank at the left that best completes the statement.

_____ **1.** The bisector of the vertex angle of an isosceles triangle also bisects ___?___.

_____ **2.** An equilateral triangle is also ___?___.

_____ **3.** One and only one ___?___ can be drawn to a line from a point outside the line.

_____ **4.** An exterior angle of a triangle is (greater than, equal to, less than) either opposite interior angle.

**PROOF:** Fill in the steps to complete the proof.

**5.** Given: *AC = BD,* and *AB* and *CD* bisect each other.
Prove: ∠A = ∠B

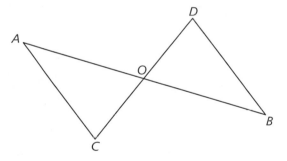

| Proof: Statements | Reasons |
| --- | --- |
|  |  |

Name _____   Date _____   Score _____

*Plane Geometry*

**COMPLETION:** Write the word(s) in the blank at the left that best completes the statement.

_____   **1.** To show that a given statement is true by proving that all other possibilities lead to a contradiction is the ___?___ method of proof.

_____   **2.** The converse of a theorem is (always, sometimes, never) true.

_____   **3.** The converse of a definition is (always, sometimes, never) true.

**PROOF:** Fill in the steps to complete the proof.

**4.** Given: $EB = EC$, $AB = DC$
   Prove: $\angle A = \angle D$

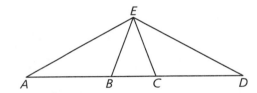

| Proof: Statements | Reasons |
|---|---|
|  |  |

Name _____ Date _____ Score _____

**COMPLETION:** Write the word(s) in the blank at the left that best completes the statement.

_____ **1.** A line that intersects two or more other lines is a(n) __?__ .

_____ **2.** Two lines perpendicular to the same line are __?__ to each other.

_____ **3.** Two parallel lines and a transversal can (always, sometimes, never) form a triangle.

_____ **4.** Two lines parallel to the same line are __?__ to each other.

**ANGLES:** Use the figure below to answer questions 5–10.

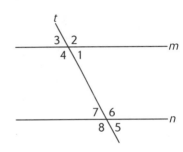

_____ **5.** Angles 1 and 7 are known as __?__ angles.

_____ **6.** Angles 2 and 6 are known as __?__ angles.

_____ **7.** Angles 3 and 5 are known as __?__ angles.

_____ **8.** If $m$ and $n$ are parallel, and $\angle 3 = 63°$, find the measure of $\angle 6$.

_____ **9.** If $m$ and $n$ are **not** parallel and $\angle 8 = 125°$, can $\angle 4 = 55°$?

_____ **10.** If $m$ and $n$ are parallel, what relationship exists between angles 1 and 6?

Name _____ Date _____ Score _____

**QUIZ 13**                                                 *Plane Geometry*

Sections 2.11–2.13

**COMPLETION:** Write the word(s) in the blank at the left that best completes the statement.

_____ 1. A straight line perpendicular to one of two parallel lines is __?__ to the other also.

_____ 2. Lines perpendicular to non-parallel lines are __?__ .

_____ 3. If two angles have their sides parallel, right side to left side and left side to right side, the angles are __?__ .

_____ 4. If two angles have their sides perpendicular, right side to right side and left side to left side, the angles are __?__ .

_____ 5. An exterior angle of a triangle is (greater than, equal to, less than) the sum of the two opposite interior angles.

_____ 6. In any right triangle, the two acute angles are __?__ .

_____ 7. Each angle of an equilateral triangle is __?__ .

_____ 8. If two parallel lines are cut by a transversal, the sum of the two interior angles on the same side of the transversal is equal to __?__ .

_____ 9. The sum of the angles of a triangle is __?__ .

_____ 10. If two angles of one triangle are equal respectively to two angles of another triangle, then the third angle of the first triangle __?__ .

**QUIZ 14**                                                                *Plane Geometry*

**COMPLETION:** Write the word(s) in the blank at the left that best completes the statement.

_____  1.  The sum of the four angles of a quadrilateral is equal to ___?___ .

_____  2.  The perpendicular to the base of an isosceles triangle that passes through the vertex will also ___?___ the vertex angle.

_____  3.  The shortest line that can be drawn from a point to a line is the ___?___ .

**PROOF:** Fill in the steps to complete the proof.

4.  Given: $AB > BD$, $\angle ADB = \angle C$
    Prove: $AD > DC$

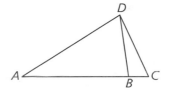

| **Proof: Statements** | **Reasons** |
| --- | --- |
|  |  |

Name _____ Date _____ Score _____

**TEST 3** (Nine-weeks Exam)                                               *Plane Geometry*

Sections 1.1–2.16

**TRUE/FALSE:** Write *true* if the statement is always true; write *false* if it is not always true.

_____  1.  When two straight lines are cut by a transversal, and the interior angles on the same side of the transversal contain 110° and 70°, the two lines are parallel.

_____  2.  If a line is parallel to one of two perpendicular lines, it is also parallel to the other line.

_____  3.  If two angles are supplementary to the same angle, they are supplementary to each other.

_____  4.  The sum of two acute angles is an obtuse angle.

_____  5.  If *AB* is the perpendicular bisector of segment *CD*, then *AB* passes through the midpoint of *CD*.

_____  6.  If two adjacent angles are supplementary, then their two exterior sides are perpendicular.

_____  7.  Two triangles are congruent if three sides of one triangle are equal respectively to three sides of the other triangle.

_____  8.  If only two angles of a triangle are equal, it will logically follow *(not necessarily in one step)* that the triangle is isosceles.

_____  9.  If two adjacent angles are complementary, a side of one of the angles is perpendicular to a side of the other angle.

_____  10.  If two sides of a triangle are unequal, the angle opposite the greater side is the smaller angle.

(continued)

**SHORT ANSWER:** Answer the following in the space provided.

**11.** List five reasons for proving two triangles are congruent. *(Abbreviations are acceptable.)*

_____

_____

**12.** List three general ways to prove that two angles are equal, excluding **definition.**

_____

_____

_____

**13.** What must two angles share in common in order to be called adjacent?

_____

**14.** Write the parallel postulate. _____

_____

**15.** What is the supplement of a 47° angle? _____

**16.** What is the complement of a 36°27' angle? _____

**COMPLETION:** Write the word(s) in the blank at the left that best completes the statement.

_____ **17.** The sum of the angles of a triangle is __?__ .

_____ **18.** A general statement accepted without proof to be true is a(n) __?__ .

_____ **19.** The measure of each angle of an equilateral triangle is __?__ degrees.

_____ **20.** When two lines intersect, they form vertical angles that are __?__ .

Name _____

_____  **21.** A statement that is not self-evident but proved by a chain of reasoning is a(n) __?__ .

_____  **22.** Base angles of an isosceles triangle are __?__ .

_____  **23.** A triangle having no equal sides is a(n) __?__ triangle.

_____  **24.** Two lines that form right angles are called __?__ .

_____  **25.** If two parallel lines are cut by a transversal, then the sum of the two exterior angles on one side of the transversal is __?__ .

**PARALLEL LINES:** *AC* is parallel to *DF.* Use your knowledge of parallel lines to find the required angles based upon the given information. No lines may be assumed to be equal. Each problem is unique. Write your answer in the space at the left.

_____  **26.** ∠3 = 45°.  Find ∠9.

_____  **27.** ∠7 = 120°, and ∠5 = 40°.  Find ∠1.  Show your work.

_____  **28.** ∠8 = 145°, and ∠1 = 37°.  Find ∠2.  Show your work.

_____  **29.** ∠2 = 72°, and ∠4 = 57°.  Find ∠3.  Show your work.

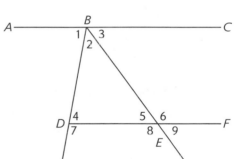

_____  **30.** ∠6 = 139°, and ∠2 = 68°.  Find ∠7.  Show your work.

**CONSTRUCTIONS:** Construct each figure according to the given description.

**31.** Construct a right triangle having *a* and *b* as its legs.

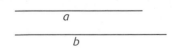

(continued)

**32.** Construct a perpendicular to *CD* from *P*.

·*P*

C ———————————————————————————— D

**PROOFS:** Fill in the steps to complete the proofs.

**33.** Given: $AC = BD$, $CB = DA$
Prove: $\triangle ABC \cong \triangle BAD$

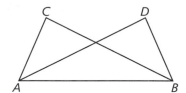

| Proof: Statements | Reasons |
|---|---|
|  |  |

**34.** Given: *AB* and *CD* bisect each other.
    Prove: *AC* = *BD* and *AC* ∥ *BD*

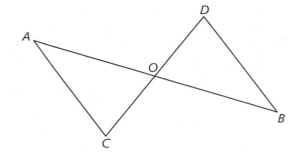

| **Proof: Statements** | **Reasons** |
| --- | --- |
|  |  |

(continued)

**35.** Given: $AB = AC$, $\angle 1 = \angle 2$
Prove: $\angle B = \angle C$

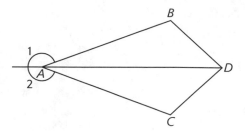

| **Proof: Statements** | **Reasons** |
| --- | --- |
|  |  |

Name _____ Date _____ Score _____

**COMPLETION:** Write the word(s) in the blank at the left that best completes the statement.

_____ 1. The distance between two parallel lines is the length of the ___?___ drawn to one line from a point in the other.

_____ 2. A rectangle having two adjacent sides equal is a(n) ___?___ .

_____ 3. A diagonal of a parallelogram divides it into ___?___ .

_____ 4. Two parallel lines are everywhere ___?___ .

_____ 5. Any two consecutive angles of a parallelogram are ___?___ .

_____ 6. The line perpendicular to the base of a parallelogram from any point in the opposite side is the ___?___ .

_____ 7. A parallelogram one of whose angles is a right angle is a(n) ___?___ .

_____ 8. Opposite angles of a parallelogram are ___?___ .

**PARALLELOGRAM:** List four ways to prove that a quadrilateral is a parallelogram. *(6 possible)*

9. _____

10. _____

11. _____

12. _____

_____

Name _____  Date _____  Score _____

**QUIZ 16** _____  *Plane Geometry*

**COMPLETION:** Write the word(s) in the blank at the left that best completes the statement.

_____  1.  A quadrilateral with two and only two sides parallel is a(n) __?__ .

_____  2.  The median to the hypotenuse of a right triangle equals __?__ .

_____  3.  The diagonals of an isosceles trapezoid are __?__ .

_____  4.  The median of a trapezoid __?__ the two diagonals.

_____  5.  A polygon that is both equilateral and equiangular is __?__ .

_____  6.  The sum of the angles of a 7-sided polygon is __?__ degrees. Show your work.

_____  7.  An equiangular polygon with 120° vertex angles has __?__ sides. Show your work.

_____  8.  The line joining the midpoints of the legs of a trapezoid is called the __?__ .

_____  9.  The diagonals of a rectangle are __?__ .

**RHOMBUS:** List two facts about the diagonals of a rhombus that are not true of parallelograms in general.

10.  _____

11.  _____

Name _____ Date _____ Score _____

**COMPLETION:** Write the word(s) in the blank at the left that best completes the statement.

_____ 1. A line drawn from a vertex of a triangle to the midpoint of the opposite side is a(n) __?__ of the triangle.

_____ 2. To locate the *incenter* of a triangle, one must bisect the __?__ of the triangle.

_____ 3. The three altitudes of a triangle meet at a point called the __?__.

_____ 4. To find the point that is equidistant from the sides of a triangle, one must construct the __?__ of the triangle.

_____ 5. If the median to one side of a triangle is equal to half that side of the triangle, then it is a(n) __?__ triangle.

_____ 6. Three or more lines that meet in a point are said to be __?__.

_____ 7. The three perpendicular bisectors of a triangle meet at a point called the __?__ of the triangle.

_____ 8. To locate a point equidistant from the vertices of a triangle, one must draw the __?__ of the triangle.

**QUIZ 18**

**PROOF:** Fill in the steps to complete the proof.

Given: $AC = BC$, $AF$ and $BF$ bisect angles $A$ and $B$
respectively, and $AD = BE$
Prove: $\angle FDE = \angle FED$

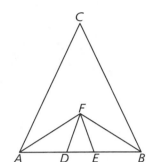

| **Proof: Statements** | **Reasons** |
| --- | --- |
| | |

Name _____ Date _____ Score _____

**TRUE/FALSE:** Write *true* if the statement is always true; write *false* if it is not always true.

_____ 1. A rhombus is equiangular.

_____ 2. A trapezoid has at least one acute angle.

_____ 3. The median of a trapezoid bisects the bases of the trapezoid.

_____ 4. If a quadrilateral is equilateral, then it is a square.

_____ 5. A parallelogram is defined as a quadrilateral whose opposite sides are parallel.

_____ 6. A diagonal of a parallelogram divides it into two congruent triangles.

_____ 7. The diagonals of a trapezoid are equal.

_____ 8. If the diagonals of a quadrilateral are equal, the quadrilateral is a rectangle.

_____ 9. If one angle of a parallelogram is a right angle, all of the other angles of the parallelogram are right angles also.

_____ 10. In parallelogram *ABCD*, if angle *A* is a right angle, then diagonal *AC* must be equal to diagonal *BD*.

_____ 11. If unequals are subtracted from equals, the remainders are unequal in the same order.

(continued)

**ALWAYS, SOMETIMES, NEVER:** Select the word which best completes each sentence. Then write *A*, *S*, or *N* in the blank at the left.

_____ **12.** If two parallel lines are cut by a transversal, the interior angles on the same side of the transversal are __?__ equal.

_____ **13.** The diagonals of a parallelogram __?__ bisect each other.

_____ **14.** If two sides of a quadrilateral are parallel, and the other two sides are equal, then the quadrilateral is __?__ a parallelogram.

_____ **15.** A quadrilateral, all of whose angles are equal, is __?__ a rectangle.

_____ **16.** The exterior angles at the base of an isosceles triangle are __?__ acute.

_____ **17.** The diagonals of a rectangle are __?__ equal.

_____ **18.** The diagonals of a quadrilateral __?__ divide it into four congruent triangles.

_____ **19.** The diagonals of a rectangle __?__ bisect each other.

_____ **20.** If the sum of two angles of a triangle is equal to the third angle, then two sides of the triangle are __?__ perpendicular to each other.

_____ **21.** The sum of the interior angles of a polygon is __?__ equal to the sum of the exterior angles of the polygon.

**MULTIPLE CHOICE:** Write the letter of the correct answer.

_____ **22.** It is false to state __?__ .
  **a.** a parallelogram is a quadrilateral    **c.** a rectangle is a parallelogram
  **b.** a rectangle is a square             **d.** none of these

_____ **23.** Two consecutive angles of a parallelogram are always __?__ .
  **a.** complementary                       **c.** supplementary
  **b.** equal                               **d.** none of these

_____ **24.** The sum of the exterior angles of a polygon of $n$ sides is __?__ .
  **a.** $n$ straight angles                 **c.** $n - 2$ straight angles
  **b.** 2 straight angles                   **d.** none of these

_____ **25.** Two opposite angles of a parallelogram are always __?__ .
  **a.** complementary                       **c.** supplementary
  **b.** equal                               **d.** none of these

_____ **26.** Medians of a triangle meet at a point called the __?__ .
          **a.** centroid             **d.** orthocenter
          **b.** incenter             **e.** none of these
          **c.** circumcenter

_____ **27.** Three lines that intersect at the same point are called __?__ .
          **a.** axiomatic            **d.** diagonal
          **b.** common             **e.** none of these
          **c.** concurrent

_____ **28.** The angle bisectors of a triangle meet at the __?__ .
          **a.** centroid             **d.** orthocenter
          **b.** incenter              **e.** none of these
          **c.** circumcenter

_____ **29.** Each angle of a regular octagon is __?__ . Show your work.
          **a.** 45°             **d.** 145°
          **b.** 90°             **e.** none of these
          **c.** 125°

_____ **30.** The distance from a vertex of a triangle to the opposite side is the length of a(n) __?__ .
          **a.** median            **d.** altitude
          **b.** angle bisector            **e.** none of these
          **c.** diagonal

_____ **31.** Parallel lines included between parallel lines are __?__ .
          **a.** complementary           **c.** exterior
          **b.** equal             **d.** none of these

**COMPLETION:** Write the word(s) in the blank at the left that best completes the statement.

_____ **32.** The midpoint of the hypotenuse of a right triangle is equidistant from __?__ .

_____ **33.** A line which joins the midpoints of two sides of a triangle is _(33)_ and equals _(34)_ .

_____ **34.**

_____ **35.** If two lines are cut by a transversal, making two equal alternate interior angles, then the sum of the two interior angles on the same side of the transversal is __?__ degrees.

(continued)

_____ **36.** The median of a trapezoid is __?__ to the bases of the trapezoid.

_____ **37.** Each angle of an equilateral triangle contains __?__ degrees.

_____ **38.** A trapezoid with nonparallel sides equal is __?__.

_____ **39.** The sum of the angles of a pentagon is __?__. Show your work.

_____ **40.** *A rectangle having two adjacent sides equal* is the definition of a(n) __?__.

_____ **41.** In a triangle, the line drawn from any vertex to the midpoint of the opposite side is a(n) __?__ of the triangle.

**PROOF:** Fill in the steps to complete the proof.

**42.** Given: Parallelogram *ABCD* with *E* and *K* on diagonal *BD, DE = BK*
Prove: *AKCE* is a parallelogram.

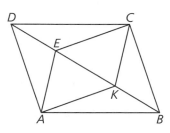

| Proof: Statements | Reasons |
|---|---|
| | |

Name _____ Date _____ Score _____

**COMPLETION:** Write the word(s) in the blank at the left that best completes the statement.

_____ 1. Any side of a triangle is (greater than, equal to, less than) the sum of the other two sides.

_____ 2. In a 30-60-90 triangle, the hypotenuse is ___?___ the shortest leg.

**PROOF:** Fill in the steps to complete the proof.

3. Given: $AB = AD$, and $\angle B > \angle D$
   Prove: $DC > BC$

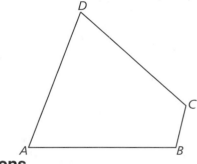

| **Proof: Statements** | **Reasons** |
| --- | --- |
|  |  |

Name _____ Date _____ Score _____

**QUIZ 20**                                                           *Plane Geometry*
_____
                                                                Sections 2.35–2.36

**COMPLETION:** Write the word(s) in the blank at the left that best completes the statement.

_____   **1.** If two sides of a triangle are 7″ and 5″, then the third side must be less than ___?___ .

_____   **2.** Referring to number 1, the third side must be greater than ___?___ .

_____   **3.** If the length of the median to the hypotenuse of a right triangle is 6 inches long, then the length of the hypotenuse is ___?___ .

_____   **4.** If a base angle of an isosceles triangle is 16° more than half of the measure of its vertex angle, then the vertex angle is ___?___ °. Show your work.

**MEASURES:** Find the values based on the descriptions.

_____   **5.** If the median of a trapezoid is 8″, and one base is 4″ more than the other base, find the length of the bases. Show your work.

_____   **6.** If an exterior angle of a triangle is 111°, and one of the opposite interior angles is twice the other, then find the three angles of the triangle. Show your work.

_____   **7.** One of two complementary angles is 18° less than three times the other angle. Find the two angles. Show your work.

61

**QUIZ 21**

**PROOFS:** Fill in the steps to complete the proofs.

1. Given: Parallelogram *ABCD* with *AE* such that $\angle a > \angle b$
   Prove: *BC > DE*

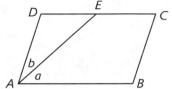

| **Proof: Statements** | **Reasons** |
| --- | --- |
| | |

(continued)

**2.** Given: $\triangle ABC$, with midpoints at $D$, $E$, and $F$
Prove: $\triangle ADF \cong \triangle FEC$

| Proof: Statements | Reasons |
|---|---|
| | |

Name _____ Date _____ Score _____

**COMPLETION:** Write the word(s) in the blank at the left that best completes the statement.

_____ 1. An angle that is formed by two radii of a circle is a(n) __?__ angle.

_____ 2. The greatest chord in a circle is the __?__.

_____ 3. Two circles are congruent if they have __?__.

_____ 4. The greater chord of a circle subtends the (greater, lesser) minor arc.

_____ 5. An arc of a circle that is greater than a semicircle is a(n) __?__ arc.

_____ 6. All radii of a circle are __?__.

_____ 7. A straight line can intersect a circle in at most __?__ point(s).

_____ 8. Two arcs of equal circles are equal if __?__ can be made to coincide.

Name _____  Date _____  Score _____

**QUIZ 23**

**COMPLETION:** Write the word(s) in the blank at the left that best completes the statement.

_____  1.  A diameter that bisects a chord of a circle, __(1)__ and __(2)__ .

_____  2.

_____  3.  The perpendicular bisector of any chord passes through __?__ .

_____  4.  Chords equidistant from the center of a circle __?__ .

_____  5.  The greater of two chords is (nearer to, farther from) the center of the circle.

_____  6.  A polygon that is inscribed in a circle must have all of its __?__ on the circle.

_____  7.  If two diameters of a circle are perpendicular to each other, then any chord parallel to one diameter is __?__ the other diameter.

_____  8.  A straight line that has only one point in common with a circle, no matter how far it is extended, is a __?__ of the circle.

_____  9.  At the point of tangency, a tangent to a circle is __?__ to the radius.

_____  10. Tangents to a circle at the ends of a diameter are __?__ to each other.

Name _____ Date _____ Score _____

**TEST 5** _____ *Plane Geometry*

**TRUE/FALSE:** Write *true* if the statement is always true; write *false* if it is not always true.

_____ 1. A diameter that bisects a shorter chord of the same circle is also perpendicular to that chord.

_____ 2. In a circle, the longer of two chords is farther from the center.

_____ 3. A perpendicular to a tangent at the point of tangency will pass through the center of a circle.

_____ 4. The greater of two minor arcs in a circle will subtend the lesser of two chords.

_____ 5. A diameter of a circle is the longest possible chord in the circle.

_____ 6. A polygon, all of whose vertices lie on a circle, is circumscribed about the circle.

**ALWAYS, SOMETIMES, NEVER:** Select the word which best completes each sentence. Then write *A, S,* or *N* in the blank at the left.

_____ 7. A line passing through the midpoint of a chord ___?___ passes through the center of the circle.

_____ 8. If two arcs of a circle are equal, the chords that they subtend are ___?___ parallel.

_____ 9. Arcs whose endpoints have been made to coincide are ___?___ equal.

_____ 10. Circles that have equal radii are ___?___ congruent circles.

_____ 11. The greater of two chords in congruent circles ___?___ subtends the lesser minor arc.

_____ 12. A quadrilateral whose opposite angles are equal is ___?___ a parallelogram.

**COMPLETION:** Write the word(s) in the blank at the left that best completes the statement.

_____ 13. A tangent to a circle is ___?___ to the radius of the circle drawn to the point of tangency.

_____ 14. An angle formed by two radii of a circle is a(n) ___?___ angle.

_____ 15. A straight line can cut a circle in at most ___?___ point(s).

_____ 16. Tangents drawn to a circle at the ends of a diameter are ___?___ to each other.

(continued)

_____ **17.** Congruent circles coincide when their __?__ are made to coincide.

_____ **18.** If two diameters are perpendicular to each other, then any chord parallel to one of them is __?__ the other diameter.

_____ **19.** An arc of a circle that is less than a semicircle is a(n) __?__ arc.

_____ **20.** When all the sides of a polygon are tangent to a circle, then the polygon is a __?__ polygon.

**PROOFS:** Fill in the steps to complete the proofs.

**21.** Given: $AB \parallel CD$ with $AE = DF$, $CE$ and
  $BF$ are both perpendicular to $AD$
  Prove: $BF = CE$

| **Proof: Statements** | **Reasons** |
| --- | --- |
|  |  |

**22.** Given: ∠*ABC* = ∠*CDA, AP = CP*
    Prove: arc *AB* = arc *CD*

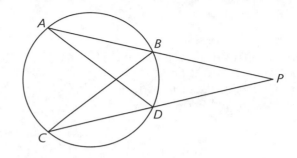

| **Proof: Statements** | **Reasons** |
| --- | --- |
|  |  |

(continued)

**23.** Given: *B* is the midpoint of arc *AC* with
radii *OA* and *OC*
Prove: *B* is equidistant from *OA* and *OC*

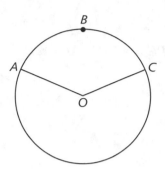

| **Proof: Statements** | Reasons |
|---|---|
| | |

**QUIZ 24**                                                                                 *Plane Geometry*

**COMPLETION:** Write the word(s) in the blank at the left that best completes the statement.

_____   1.  An unlimited line that cuts a circle in two points is a(n) ___?___.

_____   2.  A figure bounded by an arc of a circle and the chord it subtends is a(n) ___?___ of the circle.

_____   3.  Two magnitudes of the same kind that have no common unit of measure are called ___?___.

_____   4.  A central angle of a circle is measured by ___?___.

_____   5.  Two circles that have the same center, but have different radii, are said to be ___?___.

_____   6.  Tangents drawn to a circle from an external point are ___?___.

_____   7.  The line segment joining the two points of intersection of two intersecting circles is called a(n) ___?___.

_____   8.  A line that is tangent to two circles that lie on opposite sides of that line is said to be a common ___?___ tangent.

_____   9.  Two circles that are externally tangent to each other can have ___?___ common tangents.

**QUIZ 25**                                                                                    *Plane Geometry*

**ANGLES:** Find the size of each angle or arc.

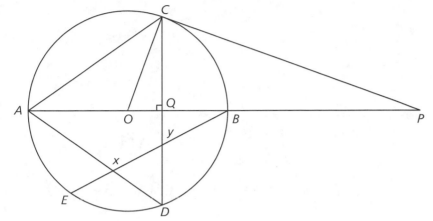

In circle *O*, arc *AC* equals 110°, and *E* is the midpoint of arc *AD*. Notice *PA* ⊥ *CD*.

_____    **1.** ∠*AOC*

_____    **2.** ∠*P*

_____    **3.** arc *BD*

_____    **4.** ∠*D*

_____    **5.** ∠*PCD*

_____    **6.** arc *AE*

_____    **7.** ∠*y*

_____    **8.** ∠*BOC*

**COMPLETION:** Write the word(s) in the blank at the left that best completes the statement.

_____    **9.** An angle inscribed in a semicircle is ___?___ .

_____    **10.** All angles inscribed in the same segment or in equal segments are ___?___ .

**QUIZ 26**

**PROOF:** Fill in the steps to complete the proof.

Given: *AB* = *CD* = *AE,* and *AE* and *CD* are parallel.
Prove: arc *EC* = arc *BC*

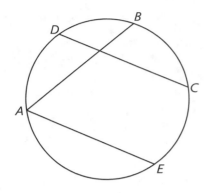

| **Proof: Statements** | **Reasons** |
|---|---|
| | |

Name _____ Date _____ Score _____

**TEST 6** (Semester Exam)　　　　　　　　　　　　　　　　*Plane Geometry*

Sections 1.1–3.19

**TRUE/FALSE:** Write *true* if the statement is always true; write *false* if it is not always true.

_____ 1. The sum of two obtuse angles can add up to a straight angle.

_____ 2. If *AB* is perpendicular to *CD*, *AB* passes through the midpoint of line segment *CD*.

_____ 3. If two chords intercept equal arcs on a circle, the chords are equidistant from the center of the circle.

_____ 4. A median divides a triangle into two congruent triangles.

_____ 5. If two angles are complementary to the same angle, they are complementary to each other.

_____ 6. A bisector of a chord passes through the center of the circle.

_____ 7. Equal chords must subtend equal arcs on the same circle or congruent circles.

_____ 8. In two circles, equal central angles will intercept arcs that have an equal number of arc degrees.

_____ 9. At least one common tangent can always be drawn to any two circles.

_____ 10. Two parallel chords of a circle intercept equal arcs between them.

_____ 11. A line which passes through the midpoint of an arc and the midpoint of its subtended chord will pass through the center of the circle as well.

_____ 12. If two chords of a circle are perpendicular to each other, then at least one of them is a diameter of the circle.

_____ 13. A diameter which bisects one of two parallel chords, both of which are not diameters, will bisect the other chord also.

(continued)

_____ **14.** Two externally tangent circles can have only two common tangents.

_____ **15.** Two circles coincide when they have the same radius.

**ALWAYS, SOMETIMES, NEVER:** Select the word which best completes each sentence. Then write *A, S,* or *N* in the blank at the left.

_____ **16.** If two angles have a common vertex, they are ___?___ adjacent.

_____ **17.** If the three angles of a triangle are equal, the triangle is ___?___ equilateral.

_____ **18.** If two isosceles triangles have unequal vertex angles, they are ___?___ congruent.

_____ **19.** The diagonals of a rectangle are ___?___ equal.

_____ **20.** If two arcs of a circle are equal, the chords of these arcs are ___?___ equal.

_____ **21.** Tangents drawn from an external point to a circle ___?___ make equal angles with the chord joining their points of tangency.

_____ **22.** Quadrilateral *ABCD* is circumscribed about a circle whose center is the point *O*. The bisector of angle *A* ___?___ passes through point *C*.

_____ **23.** If two circles are concentric, any two chords of the larger circle which are tangent to the smaller circle are ___?___ equal.

_____ **24.** An angle inscribed in an arc which contains more than 180° is ___?___ obtuse.

_____ **25.** Consecutive pairs of angles in a parallelogram are ___?___ supplementary.

_____ **26.** If two arcs have endpoints that can be made to coincide, they are ___?___ equal.

_____ **27.** A major arc is ___?___ less than a semicircle.

_____ **28.** A center segment of two circles is ___?___ less than the length of either common external tangent.

_____ **29.** In a circle, the greater of two chords is ___?___ nearer to the center of the circle.

_____ **30.** Equal chords in two different circles ___?___ subtend equal arcs.

Name _____

**ANGLES:** Find the size of each angle or arc.  Show your work.

In circle *O,* arc *DC* = 90°, ∠*C* = 40°,
arc *BC* = 90°, arc *ED* = 50°,
*PA* is tangent to the circle at *A,*
and *RD* is tangent at *D.*

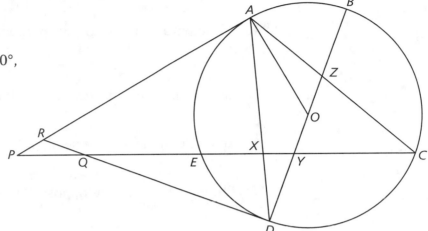

_____ **31.** arc *EA*

_____ **32.** arc *AB*

_____ **33.** ∠*DOA*

_____ **34.** ∠*OAD*

_____ **35.** ∠*DAC*

_____ **36.** ∠*CAP*

_____ **37.** ∠*BYC*

_____ **38.** ∠*APC*

_____ **39.** ∠*AOB*

_____ **40.** ∠*DRA*

**COMPLETION:** Write the word(s) in the blank at the left that best completes the statement.

_____ **41.**  The sum of an angle and its complement is ___?___ .

_____ **42.**  A line which joins the midpoints of two sides of a triangle is ___?___ to
the third side.

(continued)

_____ 43. A quadrilateral that has only two sides parallel is a(n) __?__ .

_____ 44. A line parallel to one of two perpendicular lines is __?__ to the other line.

_____ 45. Two circles are congruent if they have equal __?__ .

_____ 46. An angle inscribed in a semicircle is a(n) __?__ angle.

_____ 47. Tangents to a circle at opposite ends of a diameter are __?__ to each other.

_____ 48. A line that intersects a circle in two points is a(n) __?__ .

_____ 49. A diameter that is perpendicular to a chord will __?__ the chord.

_____ 50. The sum of the interior angles of a pentagon is __?__ . Show your work.

Name _____

**PROOFS:** Fill in the steps to complete the proofs.

**51.**  Given: $AB = CD$ and both extended to
             point $P$ outside the circle
         Prove: $\triangle ADP$ is isosceles.

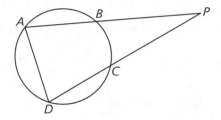

| **Proof: Statements** | **Reasons** |
| --- | --- |
| | |
| | |
| | |
| | |
| | |
| | |
| | |
| | |

(continued)

**52.** Given: *BC* is a diameter of circle *O*, and
radius *OE* is parallel to chord *CD*.
Prove: arc *BE* = arc *ED*

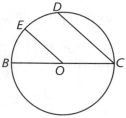

| **Proof: Statements** | **Reasons** |
| --- | --- |
| | |

**QUIZ 27** *Plane Geometry*

**CONSTRUCTIONS:** Construct each figure according to the given description.

1. Construct a line through the given point that is parallel to the given line.

2. Construct the bisector of the given arc.

3. By construction, divide the given segment into three equal parts.

Name _____  Date _____  Score _____

*Plane Geometry*

**CONSTRUCTIONS:** Construct each figure according to the given description.

**1.** Construct the circumscribed circle.

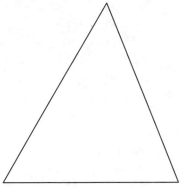

**2.** Construct a tangent to the given circle from point *P*.

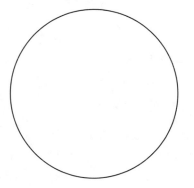

•*P*

**3.** Inscribe a circle in the given triangle.

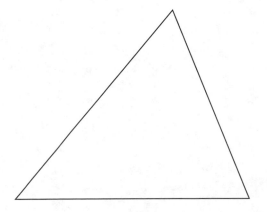

Name _____ Date _____ Score _____

**QUIZ 29**                                                                                      *Plane Geometry*

**LOCUS:** Describe the required locus.

1.  Name the locus of points equidistant from two parallel lines. _____

    _____

    _____

    _____

2.  Name that locus of points equidistant from two intersecting lines. _____

    _____

    _____

    _____

3.  Name the locus of points that is equidistant from two given points. _____

    _____

    _____

    _____

4.  Name the locus of points equidistant from the sides of a triangle. _____

    _____

    _____

    _____

5.  Describe the locus of points that is five inches from a given point. _____

    _____

    _____

    _____

**QUIZ 30** _____ *Plane Geometry*

**LOCI:** Describe the required loci and draw a figure in the space at the right.

1. Name the locus of points that is five
   inches from a given point and ten inches
   away from a given line that is five inches
   from the given point.

   _____

   _____

   _____

   _____

   _____

   _____

2. Name all possible loci that are a given
   distance from a given point and also
   equidistant from any two other points.

   _____

   _____

   _____

   _____

   _____

   _____

   _____

Name _____  Date _____  Score _____

**CONSTRUCTIONS:** Construct each figure according to the given description.

1. Construct a right triangle with the two
   given segments as its legs.  (Label the legs
   corresponding to the given segments.)

2. Construct an isosceles triangle with the
   given base and altitude.

3. Construct a parallelogram with the given
   adjacent sides and the given included angle
   of those sides.

Name _____ Date _____ Score _____

**COMPLETION:** Write the word(s) in the blank at the left that best completes the statement.

_____    **1.** Name the four major parts of a construction problem.

_____

_____

_____

_____    **2.** Name the two key terms relating to a locus of points in that your described locus contains <u>only</u> those points and <u>all</u> those points that satisfy the stated conditions.

_____

**CONSTRUCTIONS:** Construct each figure according to the given description.

**3.** Divide *AB* into 5 equal segments.

                              *A* _____ *B*

(continued)

**4.** Construct a tangent to the circle from point *R*.

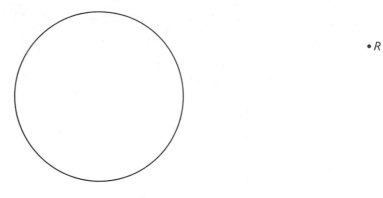

•*R*

**5.** Circumscribe a circle about the given triangle.

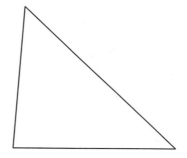

**6.** Construct a tangent to circle *O* at *P*.

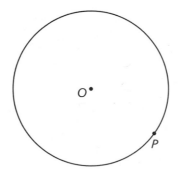

7. Construct a right triangle given a leg and its opposite acute angle.

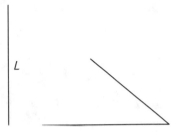

8. Construct an isosceles triangle with the given leg and base.

_____ *L* _____

_____ *B* _____

**LOCI:** Describe the required loci and draw a figure in the space at the right.

9. What is the locus of points outside a circle and a distance *d* from the circle?

_____

_____

_____

_____

_____

_____

(continued)

10. What is the locus of the centers of all circles that are tangent to both of two parallel lines?

_____

_____

_____

_____

_____

_____

11. What is the locus of points in the interior of the square *ABCD* <u>and</u> <u>also</u> equidistant from its sides *AB* and *BC?*

_____

_____

_____

_____

_____

12. What is the locus of points that is two inches from a given line <u>and</u> <u>also</u> three inches from a given point in that line?

_____

_____

_____

_____

_____

_____

13. What is the locus of points equidistant from points *A* and *B,* which are six inches apart, <u>and</u> <u>also</u> five inches away from point *A?*

_____

_____

_____

_____

_____

_____

**14.** Given two circles concentric at *O* and with radii of six and ten inches, and given the straight line *AB* through point *O;* what is the locus of points that is equidistant from the two circles, <u>and</u> <u>also</u> at a distance of eight inches from line *AB?*

_____

_____

_____

_____

_____

_____

_____

_____

Name _____ Date _____ Score _____

**PROPORTIONS:** Name the proportion transformation used to change each of the following.

_____ **1.** $\frac{2}{3} = \frac{8}{12}$ into $\frac{5}{3} = \frac{20}{12}$

_____ **2.** $\frac{a}{b} = \frac{c}{d}$ into $\frac{a}{c} = \frac{b}{d}$

_____ **3.** $\frac{a}{b} = \frac{c}{d}$ into $\frac{b}{a} = \frac{d}{c}$

**SHORT ANSWER:** Answer the following in the space provided. Show your work for problems 6–9.

_____ **4.** Name the first term in a ratio.

_____ **5.** Give the term for an equality of ratios.

_____ **6.** Solve for $x$: $\frac{5}{7} = \frac{x}{35}$

_____ **7.** Solve for $x$: $\frac{3}{4} = \frac{12}{x-3}$

_____ **8.** Find the fourth proportional of 2, 5, and 8.

_____ **9.** Find the mean proportional of 3 and 12.

**10.** In the space below, use the fundamental property of proportions to show that $\frac{3}{5} = \frac{36}{60}$.

**QUIZ 33**                                                           *Plane Geometry*

Sections 4.4–4.7

**LINES:** Solve for the required line using the diagram beside each question. Show your work.

_____  **1.** If *DE* ‖ *AB*, *CE* = 6, *BE* = 3, and *AC* = 12, then *AD* = ___?___.

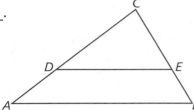

_____  **2.** If *XZ* = 6, *YZ* = 12, and *XW* = 3, then *XY* = ___?___.

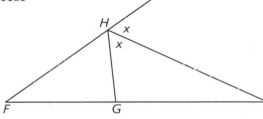

∠1 = ∠2

_____  **3.** If *FH* = 10, *GH* = 6, *GJ* = 15, and *JH* is an exterior angle bisector, then find *FG*.

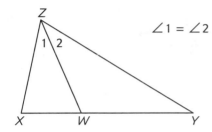

**PROOF:** Fill in the steps to complete the proof.

**4.** Given: *AC* ‖ *DB*
   Prove: △*ACO* ~ △*BDO*

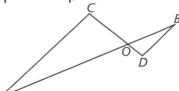

| Proof: Statements | Reasons |
|---|---|
|  |  |
|  |  |
|  |  |
|  |  |
|  |  |

Name _____ Date _____ Score _____

**QUIZ 34**                                                                *Plane Geometry*

Sections 4.8–4.10

**LINES:** Solve for the required line using the diagram below.  Show your work.

$AC \perp BC$, $CD \perp AB$

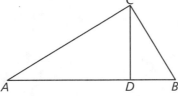

_____ **1.** If $AB = 8\frac{1}{3}$, and $BD = 3$, then $BC = \underline{\ ?\ }$.

_____ **2.** With the same conditions as number one, $AC = \underline{\ ?\ }$.

_____ **3.** With the same conditions as number one, $CD = \underline{\ ?\ }$.

_____ **4.** If $AD = 8$, and $CD = 4$, then $BD = \underline{\ ?\ }$.  *(Problems 4 and 5 are independent of other problems.)*

_____ **5.** If $BD = 4$, and $BC = 6$, then $AD = \underline{\ ?\ }$.

**TEST 8** _____  *Plane Geometry*

**RATIOS AND PROPORTIONS:** Determine the following ratios based upon $\frac{AB}{BC} = \frac{1}{2}$.

_____  **1.** *BC:AB*

_____  **2.** *AB:AC*

_____  **3.** *BC:AC*

_____  **4.** *AC:BC*

A •——————————• B ———————————————————• C

_____  **5.** Which of the following is not a true statement?
(a) 5:10 = 10:20  (b) 3:4 = 15:30  (c) 2:3 = 24:36

**PROPORTIONS:** Solve for *x*.  Show your work.

_____  **6.** 20:*x* = 10:24

_____  **7.** 4:12 = *x*:*x* + 8

_____  **8.** 2*r*:*s* = *x*:*t*

**EXERCISES:** Solve the following.  Show your work for problems 9 and 10.

_____  **9.** Find the fourth proportional of: 4, 18, 16.

_____  **10.** Find the mean proportional between 4 and 16.

_____  **11.** Rewrite 5:12 = 10:24 by the inversion transformation.

_____  **12.** Rewrite 4:5 = 16:20 by the alternation transformation.

_____  **13.** If $\frac{u}{v} = \frac{w}{x} = \frac{y}{z} = \frac{3}{4}$, then find $\frac{u+w+y}{v+x+z}$.

(continued)

**TRANSFORMATIONS:** Write the name of the transformation that has been performed on *a:b = c:d* to get each of the following.

_____ **14.** $a + b : b = c + d : d$

_____ **15.** $b : a = d : c$

_____ **16.** $a - b : b = c - d : d$

_____ **17.** $a : c = b : d$

_____ **18.** $a + b : a - b = c + d : c - d$

**SHORT ANSWER:** Answer the following in the space provided.

_____ **19.** What is the definition of a proportion?

_____ **20.** Name the first term of a ratio.

_____ **21.** Name the second term of a ratio.

_____ **22.** Name the first and fourth terms of a proportion.

_____ **23.** Name the second and third terms of a proportion.

_____ **24.** What is the special name for the fourth term in the proportion $a{:}b = b{:}c?$

**25.** Write the fundamental property of proportions.

_____

_____

_____

26. Name the two conditions for figures in geometry to be called similar based on the definition.

    (1)_____

    (2)_____

27. What is the special name for the ratio of any pair of corresponding sides of similar polygons?

    _____

**TRIANGLES:** Solve the following. Show your work.

_____ **28.** $WZ = 6$, $ZX = 8$, and $WY = 9$. Find $XY$.

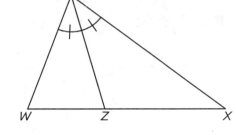

_____ **29.** $RS = 6$, $RT = 3$, and $TS = 4\frac{1}{2}$. Find $MR$.

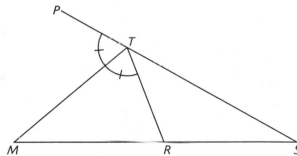

_____ **30.** Given: $DE \parallel AB$, $AC = 15$, $DC = 10$, and $EC = 8$. Find $BE$.

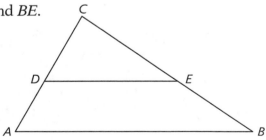

_____ **31.** If $AC = 12$, $BE = 3$, $AD = 4$, and $EC = 6$, is $DE$ parallel to $AB$?

(continued)

**PROOF:** Fill in the steps to complete the proof.

**32.** Given: Isosceles $\triangle ABC$ with $AD = AB$
      Prove: $\triangle BDA \sim \triangle ABC$

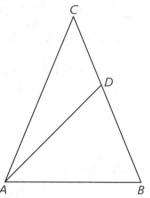

| **Proof: Statements** | **Reasons** |
| --- | --- |
|  |  |

**QUIZ 35** _____ *Plane Geometry*

Sections 4.12–4.14

**LINES:** Solve for each required line using the diagram below. Show your work.

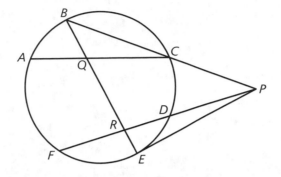

_____ **1.** If $AQ = 6$, $CQ = 8$, and $BQ = 4$, then $EQ = $ __?__ .

_____ **2.** If $PD = 4$, and $DF = 5$, then $PE = $ __?__ .

_____ **3.** If $FR = 9$, $ER = 3$, and $DR = 4$, then $BE = $ __?__ .

_____ **4.** If $PD = 5$, $FD = 7$, and $PC = 4$, then $BC = $ __?__ .

_____ **5.** If $PE = 12$, and $PC = 8$, then $BC = $ __?__ .

Name _____ Date _____ Score _____

**QUIZ 36**                                                                 *Plane Geometry*

                                                                  Sections 4.15–4.20

**PARALLEL LINES:** Solve for the following using the diagram below. Show your work.

_____ 1. If $AD = 8$, $CD = 6$, and $CE = 3$, then $BC = $ __?__ .

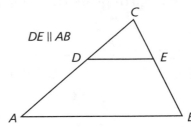

_____ 2. If $\angle CDE = 40°$, and $\angle C = 75°$, then $\angle B = $ __?__ .

**COMPLETION:** Write the word(s) in the blank at the left that best completes the statement.

_____ 3. The perimeter of a square that has a diagonal of 24 inches is __?__ .

_____ 4. The altitude of an equilateral triangle that has a side of 6 inches is __?__ .

(continued)

113

**CONSTRUCTION:** Construct the figure according to the given description.

**5.** Construct the fourth proportional to the three given line segments.

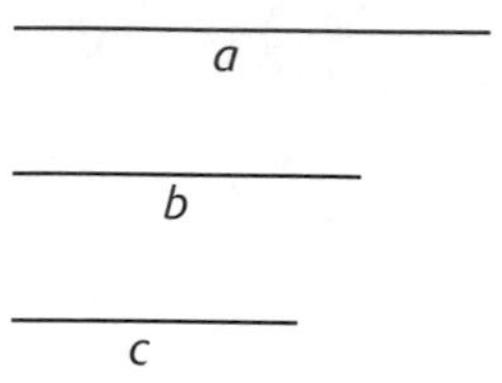

$a$

$b$

$c$

**QUIZ 37**

**CONSTRUCTIONS:** Construct each figure according to the given description.

**1.** Construct the mean proportional between the two given segments.

_____
      *a*

_____
      *b*

**2.** Construct the similar polygon to the given polygon with the given sides *a* and *a'* corresponding.

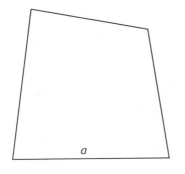

_____
          *a'*

Name _____ Date _____ Score _____

**QUIZ 38** _____ *Plane Geometry*

Sections 4.25–5.1

**COMPLETION:** Write the word(s) in the blank at the left that best completes the statement.

_____ 1. The projection of a line segment onto a perpendicular is a __?__ .

_____ 2. The projection of a segment onto a parallel line is (greater than, equal to, less than) the original segment.

_____ 3. The number of square units contained within a given surface is the __?__ .

_____ 4. A quantity which remains the same throughout a given problem or discussion is a(n) __?__ .

_____ 5. A quantity which changes throughout a given problem or discussion is called a(n) __?__ .

_____ 6. If two plane figures have different shapes, they (can, cannot) have equal areas.

_____ 7. If a variable $x$ approaches a constant $q$ so that the value of $x$ comes closer and closer to the value of $q$ but it never reaches the value of $q$, then $q$ is said to be the __?__ of $x$.

_____ 8. In right triangle *ABC* above, the projection of side *AB* upon side *AC* is (greater than, less than, equal to) side *AC*.

**PROJECTIONS:** In the diagram below, draw the required projection, label it, and describe the projection using your label(s) in the blank.

_____ 9. Draw the projection of point *C* onto *AB*.

_____ 10. Draw the projection of *DE* onto *AB*.

Name _____ Date _____ Score _____

**EXERCISES:** Solve the following exercises and write your answers in the spaces at the left. Show your work.

_____ 1. One rectangle has a base of 12 inches and an altitude of 6 inches. The other has a base of 10 inches and an altitude of 5 inches. What is the ratio of the first rectangle to the second?

_____ 2. What is the area of the first rectangle in number 1 above?

_____ 3. Find the area of a triangle that has a base of 6 inches and an altitude of 8 inches.

_____ 4. A trapezoid has one base of 10 inches, an altitude of 6 inches, and an area of 51 square inches. Find the length of the other base.

_____ 5. A parallelogram has an altitude of 8 inches and an area of 48 square inches. Find the length of its base.

_____ 6. A right triangle has a hypotenuse of 13 inches and a leg of 5 inches. Find the area of the right triangle.

_____ 7. A parallelogram has a base and an altitude that have a ratio of 4 to 3. If the area is 108 square inches, what is the measure of the base?

**TEST 9** (Nine-Weeks Exam)                                             *Plane Geometry*

Sections 3.20–5.6

**TRUE/FALSE:** Write *true* if the statement is always true; write *false* if it is not always true.

_____  1.  If the lengths of the corresponding pairs of sides of two polygons are proportional, those polygons are similar.

_____  2.  A line through the midpoints of two sides of a triangle cuts off a new triangle that is similar to the original triangle.

_____  3.  The lengths of two corresponding altitudes of similar triangles will have the same ratio as any pair of corresponding sides.

_____  4.  Doubling the lengths of the sides of similar triangles will also double the ratio of similitude of those triangles.

_____  5.  When a secant and a tangent are drawn to a circle from the same point outside of the circle, then the secant is the mean proportional between the tangent and its external segment.

_____  6.  If the legs of a right triangle are 6 and 8, then the hypotenuse is 11.

_____  7.  The altitude to the hypotenuse of a right triangle is the third proportional between the two segments of the hypotenuse that it forms.

_____  8.  Two triangles are similar if just two pairs of corresponding angles are known to be equal.

_____  9.  If in two triangles, at least one pair of corresponding sides is not proportional, then the triangles are never similar.

**MULTIPLE CHOICE:** Write the letter of the correct answer.

_____  10.  Altitude $CD$ is drawn to hypotenuse $AB$ of right triangle $ABC$.  $(AC)^2$ equals __?__ .
   **a.** $CB \times DB$                     **c.** $DB \times AD$
   **b.** $AB \times AD$                     **d.** none of these

(continued)

_____ 11. A tangent and a secant are drawn to a circle from an external point. The secant passes through the center of the circle. The external segment of the secant is 5 and the internal segment is 6. The length of the tangent to the circle is __?__.
   **a.** $\sqrt{30}$                                     **c.** $\sqrt{66}$
   **b.** $\sqrt{55}$                                     **d.** none of these

_____ 12. If the ratio of the lengths of a pair of corresponding sides in two similar triangles is 4:1, then the ratio of the lengths of a pair of corresponding altitudes is __?__.
   **a.** 4:1                                        **c.** 2:1
   **b.** 16:1                                       **d.** none of these

_____ 13. The locus of points at a given distance from a given point is __?__.
   **a.** a circle                                   **c.** two straight lines
   **b.** a straight line                            **d.** none of these

_____ 14. The locus of points a given distance from a line is __?__.
   **a.** a circle                                   **c.** two straight lines
   **b.** a straight line                            **d.** none of these

_____ 15. The locus of the centers of all circles having a given line segment as a common chord is __?__.
   **a.** a circle                                   **c.** two straight lines
   **b.** a straight line                            **d.** none of these

_____ 16. The center of a circumscribed circle about a given triangle may be found by the intersection of __?__.
   **a.** angle bisectors                            **c.** altitudes
   **b.** perpendicular bisectors of the sides  **d.** none of these

_____ 17. The fourth proportional of 2, 4, 6, is __?__.
   **a.** 8                                          **c.** 12
   **b.** 10                                         **d.** none of these

_____ 18. Two points $A$ and $B$ are 7 inches apart. How many points are 12 inches away from $A$ and **also** 4 inches apart from $B$? __?__
   **a.** 1                                          **c.** 4
   **b.** 2                                          **d.** none of these

_____ 19. Point $C$ is three inches away from a given line $AB$. How many points in $AB$ are five inches from point $C$? __?__.
   **a.** 1                                          **c.** 4
   **b.** 2                                          **d.** none of these

_____ 20. Given quadrilateral $ABCD$, the locus of points equidistant from $AB$ and $AD$ **must** include vertex $C$ if $ABCD$ is a __?__.
   **a.** trapezoid                                  **c.** parallelogram
   **b.** rectangle                                  **d.** none of these

122

Name _____

**EXERCISES:** Solve the following exercises and write your answers in the spaces at the left. Show your work.

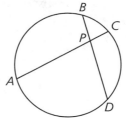

_____ 21. *BP* = 4, *DP* = 9, and *CP* = 3.  Find *AP*.

_____ 22. Find the area of a trapezoid that has an altitude of 6 inches, and the sum of the bases is 12 inches.

_____ 23. Find the area of a parallelogram that has a base of 10 inches and an altitude of 6 inches.

_____ 24. Find the altitude of a triangle that has a base of 7 inches and an area of 21 square inches.

**CONSTRUCTIONS:** Construct each figure according to the given description.

**25.** Construct the fourth proportional to *a*, *b*, and *c*.

_____
  *a*

_____
  *b*

_____
  *c*

**26.** Construct the mean proportional between segments *r* and *s*.

_____
  *r*

_____
  *s*

(continued)

**27.** On line *m*, find by construction the point that is equidistant from points *C* and *D*.

.*D*

.*C*

_____  *m*

**PROOF:** Fill in the steps to complete the proof.

**28.** Given: △*ABC* with altitudes *AD* and *CE*
Prove: $AB \cdot CE = CB \cdot AD$

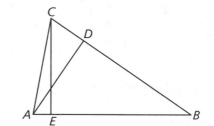

| Proof: Statements | Reasons |
|---|---|
|  |  |

Name _____  Date _____  Score _____

**QUIZ 40**  *Plane Geometry*

Sections 5.5–5.9

**EXERCISES:** Solve the following exercises and write your answers in the spaces at the left. Leave answers in radical form if applicable. Show your work.

_____ **1.** If two similar figures have areas of 48 sq. in. and 75 sq. in., and a side of the smaller figure is 4 in., find the corresponding side of the larger figure.

_____ **2.** If the hypotenuse of a right triangle is 13 in. long, and one of the legs is 5 in. long, find the length of the other leg.

_____ **3.** If two corresponding sides of two similar figures are 4 in. and 7 in. respectively, and the area of the larger is 98 sq. in., find the area of the smaller figure.

_____ **4.** If the legs of a right triangle are 7 in. and 8 in., find the area of the triangle.

Name _____ Date _____ Score _____

**QUIZ 41**                                                        *Plane Geometry*

**EXERCISES:** Solve the following exercises and write your answers in the spaces at the left. Leave answers in radical form if applicable.  Show your work.

_____  **1.** Find the altitude of an equilateral triangle that has a perimeter of 18 inches.

_____  **2.** Find the area of the triangle in number 1.

_____  **3.** Find the length of the diagonal of a square that has an area of 25 square inches.

_____  **4.** Find the area of a triangle that has sides of 7, 9, and 12 inches.

Name _____ Date _____ Score _____

**QUIZ 42** _____ *Plane Geometry*

**EXERCISES:** Solve the following exercises and write your answers in the spaces at the left. Leave answers in radical form if applicable. Show your work.

_____ 1. An altitude of an equilateral triangle is 12 inches. Find a side.

_____ 2. Find the area of the triangle in number 1.

_____ 3. Find the area of a triangle that has sides of 5, 12, and 13.

_____ 4. Find the area of a rhombus that has sides that are 10 inches long, and one of its diagonals is 12 inches long.

**QUIZ 43**

**CONSTRUCTION:** Construct a square that is equal to the given triangle.

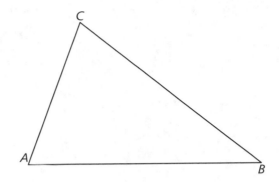

**QUIZ 44**                                                    *Plane Geometry*
                                                              Sections 5.15–5.16

**CONSTRUCTIONS:** Construct each figure according to the given description.

**1.** Construct a triangle that is equal to the given polygon (transform).

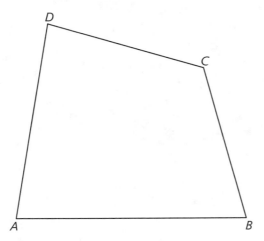

**2.** Construct a square equal to the sum of the two given squares.

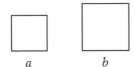

Name _____ Date _____ Score _____

**TEST 10** _____ *Plane Geometry*

**TRUE/FALSE:** Write *true* if the statement is always true; write *false* if it is not always true.

_____ **1.** If two rectangles have equal perimeters, they must have equal areas.

_____ **2.** Two equilateral triangles having equal perimeters will have equal areas.

_____ **3.** The diagonals of a parallelogram will divide it into four equal triangles.

_____ **4.** The line joining the midpoints of the bases of a trapezoid forms two similar trapezoids.

_____ **5.** A line segment which joins the midpoints of two sides of a triangle forms a triangle that is one fourth the area of the original triangle.

**MULTIPLE CHOICE:** Write the letter of the correct answer.

_____ **6.** A median of a triangle divides it into two triangles which are always ___?___ .
  **a.** congruent          **c.** equal in area
  **b.** similar            **d.** none of these

_____ **7.** If each of the dimensions of a rectangle is multiplied by 3, the area is then multiplied by ___?___ .
  **a.** 3                  **c.** $\sqrt{3}$
  **b.** 9                  **d.** none of these

_____ **8.** If the lengths of two adjacent sides of a triangle remain constant, and the degree measure of the included angle increases from 1° to 90°, then the area of the triangle ___?___ .
  **a.** increases          **c.** remains the same
  **b.** decreases          **d.** none of these

_____ **9.** If the length of each side of a triangle is multiplied by two, then the area of the triangle is multiplied by ___?___ .
  **a.** 2                  **c.** 6
  **b.** 4                  **d.** none of these

_____ **10.** If the length of each diagonal of a square is represented by *d*, then the area of the square is represented by ___?___ .
  **a.** $d$                **c.** $d^2\sqrt{2}$
  **b.** $2d$               **d.** none of these

(continued)

**CONSTRUCTIONS:** Construct each figure according to the given description.

11. Transform the given triangle *ABC* into
    a right triangle, one leg of which is
    equal in length to *AB* in triangle *ABC*.

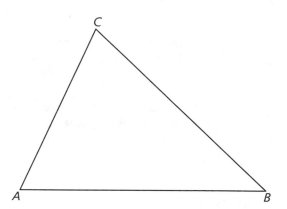

12. Transform quadrilateral *ABCD* into a triangle.

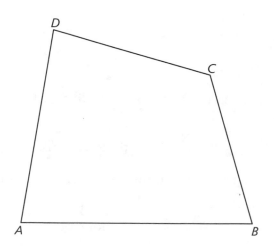

Name _____

**EXERCISES:** Solve the following exercises and write your answers in the spaces at the left. Leave answers in radical form if applicable. Show your work.

_____    **13.** A diagonal of a rectangle is 10 inches, and the base is 6 inches. Find the area of the rectangle.

_____    **14.** The equal sides of an isosceles trapezoid each measure 5, and its altitude measures 4. If the area of the trapezoid is 48, find the lengths of its bases.

_____    **15.** The sides of a triangle have lengths of 3, 4, and 5. Find the area of the triangle.

_____    **16.** Find the area of a rhombus if its diagonals are 13 inches and 8 inches.

_____    **17.** A right triangle has a hypotenuse of 17 inches and a leg of 8 inches. Find the missing leg.

(continued)

_____  **18.** Find the side of a square whose area
                          equals a triangle with an area of 28
                          square inches.

_____  **19.** Find the area of an equilateral trian-
                          gle if it has a 14 inch side.

_____  **20.** Two similar polygons have areas of
                          100 square inches and 81 square
                          inches.  If a side of the first is 5 in.,
                          find the corresponding side of the
                          second polygon.

**QUIZ 45** _____ *Plane Geometry*

**POLYGONS:** Solve and write your answers in the space at the left.  Leave your answer in radical form if applicable and show your work.

_____  **1.** How many sides will a regular polygon have if its central angle is 40°?

_____  **2.** Find the measure of an exterior angle of the polygon in number 1.

_____  **3.** Find the sum of the angles of a regular pentagon.

_____  **4.** Name the line that is drawn from the center of a regular polygon perpendicular to the sides.

_____  **5.** Find the length of the line in number 4 that is drawn in a regular hexagon that has a radius of 6 inches.

Name _____ Date _____ Score _____

**QUIZ 46** _____ *Plane Geometry*
Sections 6.2–6.5

**COMPLETION:** Write the word(s) in the blank at the left that best completes the statement.

_____ 1. The diagonals of any regular pentagon are ___?___ .

_____ 2. An angle of a regular polygon, and the angle at the center are ___?___ .

_____ 3. The line that joins the center of a regular polygon to any vertex is a(n) ___?___ .

**POLYGONS:** Solve and write your answers in the spaces at the left. Leave answers in radical form if applicable. Show your work.

_____ 4. How many sides does a regular polygon have if each angle measures 144°?

_____ 5. If the corresponding sides of two regular heptagons are 2 inches and 3 inches respectively, what is the ratio of their areas?

_____ 6. Find the area of a regular hexagon that has a 4-inch side.

Name _____  Date _____  Score _____

Section 6.6

**CIRCLES:** Solve and write your answers in the spaces at the left.  Round answers to the hundredths place if needed.  Show your work.  Use $\pi = 3.14$.

_____  1.  Find the circumference of a circle that has a 6-inch radius.

_____  2.  Find the length of a 60° arc of the circle in number 1.

_____  3.  If two circles have circumferences of $12\pi$ inches and $18\pi$ inches, find the ratio between their radii.

_____  4.  Find the diameter of a circle that has a circumference of $20\pi$ inches.

Name _____ Date _____ Score _____

**QUIZ 48**                                                    *Plane Geometry*
                                                               Sections 6.7–6.8

**CIRCLES:** Solve and write your answers in the blanks at the left.  Leave your answers in terms of
π, in radical form, and as fractions if applicable.  Show your work.

_____   1.  Find the area of a circle that has a 4-inch radius.

_____   2.  Find the diameter of a circle that has an area of 16π square inches.

_____   3.  Find the area of a 60° sector of a circle that has a 5-inch radius.

_____   4.  Find the area of a circle that has a circumference of 8π inches.

_____   5.  Find the area of a segment of a circle if its arc is 120° and the radius
                            is 3 inches.

Name _____ Date _____ Score _____

**TEST 11** _____

**TRUE/FALSE:** Write *true* if the statement is always true; write *false* if it is not always true.

_____ 1. Regular polygons of the same number of sides are similar.

_____ 2. An apothem of the regular polygon is the radius of the circumscribed circle.

_____ 3. The area of a regular polygon is equal to the product of its perimeter and its apothem.

_____ 4. A radius of a regular polygon bisects the vertex angle of the polygon to which it is drawn.

_____ 5. As the number of sides of a regular polygon inscribed in a circle increases, the length of the apothem of the polygon decreases.

_____ 6. If the radius of a circle is 2 inches, the number of square inches in the area of the circle is the same number as the number of inches in the circumference.

_____ 7. If the length of the radius of a circle is multiplied by a positive number $s$, the circumference of the circle is multiplied by $s^2$.

_____ 8. As the number of sides of a regular polygon increases, the number of degrees in the central angles of those polygons increases also.

_____ 9. The ratio of the circumference of a circle to its diameter is constant.

_____ 10. An equilateral polygon is a regular polygon.

_____ 11. A regular polygon is equiangular.

_____ 12. An equiangular polygon inscribed in a circle is regular.

(continued)

_____  **13.** A circle can be circumscribed about any regular polygon.

_____  **14.** The ratio of the areas of two circles that are not equal is the same as the ratio of the lengths of the radii of the two circles.

_____  **15.** If a circle is divided into three or more arcs, the chords of these arcs form a regular polygon.

**MULTIPLE CHOICE:** Write the letter of the correct answer.

_____  **16.** A regular decagon has a side whose length is represented by $s$ and an apothem whose length is represented by $a$. The area of the decagon is represented by __?__.
    **a.** $20as$                             **c.** $5as$
    **b.** $10as$                          **d.** none of these

_____  **17.** As the length of the radius of a circle increases, the ratio of the circumference to the diameter of the circle __?__.
    **a.** is constant                      **c.** decreases
    **b.** increases                       **d.** none of these

_____  **18.** If the length of the radius of a circle is multiplied by 4, then the area of the circle is multiplied by __?__.
    **a.** 2                                  **c.** 8
    **b.** 4                                  **d.** none of these

_____  **19.** A central angle of a regular polygon and a vertex angle of that polygon are never __?__.
    **a.** supplementary                 **c.** equal
    **b.** complementary               **d.** none of these

_____  **20.** The area of a circle with a diameter whose length is represented by $d$ is represented by __?__.
    **a.** $\frac{1}{4}\pi d^2$                          **c.** $\pi d^2$
    **b.** $\frac{1}{2}\pi d^2$                          **d.** none of these

**EXERCISES:** Solve and write your answers in the blanks at the left. Show your work.

_____  **21.** If an equilateral triangle is inscribed in a circle whose radius is 8 inches long, find the length of its apothem.

_____ **22.** If the radius of a circle is 8 inches,
find the radius of a circle whose
area is four times as large.

_____ **23.** An arc of a circle contains 72° and is
10 inches long. Find the circumfer-
ence of the circle.

_____ **24.** A circle has an area of 80 square
inches. Find the area of a sector
whose central angle contains 45°.

_____ **25.** In the semicircle, the length of
chord *AC* is 16 in., and the length of
chord *BC* is 12 in. Find the area of
the shaded region. Leave your
answer in terms of π if applicable.

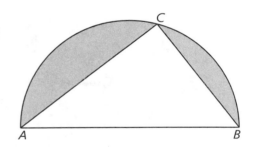

_____ **26.** If two circles have radii of 4 inches
and 10 inches respectively, then
what would be the ratio of their
circumferences?

_____ **27.** In number 26, what would be the
ratio of their areas?

(continued)

_____ **28.** If two similar polygons have corresponding sides that measure 6 and 8 inches respectively, and the area of the smaller one is 36 square inches, what would be the area of the larger polygon?

_____ **29.** Find the measure of the central angle of an 18-sided regular polygon.

_____ **30.** Find the number of sides a regular polygon will have if each vertex angle measures 150°.

Name _____  Date _____  Score _____

**EXERCISES:** Solve and write your answers in the blanks at the left.  Leave your answers in terms of π and in radical form if applicable.  Show your work.

_____  **1.** Two regular polygons with the same number of sides have sides of 6 inches and 8 inches respectively. Find the ratio of their perimeters.

_____  **2.** From number 1, what is the ratio of their areas?

_____  **3.** Find the apothem of a square that has an area of 36 square inches.

_____  **4.** What is the area of a circle that is inscribed in the square in number 3?

_____  **5.** Find the perimeter of a hexagon circumscribed about a circle that has a circumference of $12\pi$ inches.

**QUIZ 50**                                                      *Plane Geometry*

Sections 6.12–6.14

**EXERCISES:** Solve and write your answers in the blanks at the left. Leave your answers in radical form if applicable. Show your work.

_____    **1.** Find the area of an equilateral triangle inscribed in a circle that has a radius of 4 inches.

_____    **2.** Find the radius of a circle that is circumscribed about a regular hexagon that has a 24-inch perimeter.

**CONSTRUCTION:** Construct a regular hexagon given the radius of the circumscribed circle.

**3.**

_____
    *r*

Name _____ Date _____ Score _____

**TEST 12** (Final Exam)                                        *Plane Geometry*

Sections 1.1–6.15

**ALWAYS, SOMETIMES, NEVER:** Select the word which best completes each sentence. Then write *A, S,* or *N* in the blank at the left.

_____ 1. Two points __?__ determine one and only one straight line.

_____ 2. If the endpoints of a line segment are on a circle, the segment is __?__ a diameter.

_____ 3. A quadrilateral __?__ has only one diagonal.

_____ 4. If two lines are parallel to the same line, then they are __?__ parallel to each other.

_____ 5. If two lines are cut by a transversal so that the alternate interior angles are equal, the corresponding angles are __?__ equal.

_____ 6. The bisectors of a pair of corresponding angles of two lines cut by a transversal are __?__ parallel to each other.

_____ 7. The sides of a circumscribed equilateral triangle are __?__ bisected at the points of contact to the circle.

_____ 8. If two chords of a circle bisect each other, both chords are __?__ diameters.

_____ 9. A line that is perpendicular to the tangent of a circle at the point of contact will __?__ pass through the center of that circle.

_____ 10. An inscribed angle of a circle is __?__ equal to the measure of the arc it subtends.

_____ 11. An angle inscribed in a minor arc is __?__ acute.

_____ 12. If $a{:}b = c{:}d$, then $d{:}b = a{:}c$ can __?__ be obtained by performing transformations.

_____ 13. In triangles *ABC* and *RST,* if $a{:}b = r{:}s$ and angle *C* = angle *T,* then triangles *ABC* and *RST* are __?__ congruent.

_____ 14. Two triangles that are equal are __?__ congruent.

_____ 15. If two polygons have the same number of sides, then they are __?__ similar.

_____ 16. If the number of degrees in an angle is *y,* then its complement is __?__ 180° – *y.*

_____ 17. The perimeter of a regular polygon of *n* sides inscribed in a circle is __?__ less than the circumference of the circle (*n* is any integer greater than 0 and less than infinity).

(continued)

       **155**

**TRUE/FALSE:** Write *true* if the statement is always true; write *false* if it is not always true.

The two circles at the right have the same center
at point *O*. *AD* is the diameter of the larger circle,
and *AD* intersects the smaller circle at *B* and *C*.
*OF* is a radius of the larger circle, and it intersects
the smaller circle at point *E*.

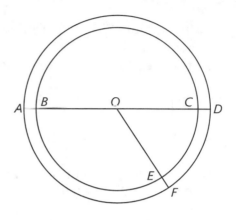

_____  **18.** Arc *EC* and arc *FD* are equal in degrees.

_____  **19.** If arc *EC* = 47 degrees, then arc *AF* = 153 degrees.

_____  **20.** The number of angle degrees in angle *FOD* is equal to the number of
                                    arc degrees in arc *EC*.

_____  **21.** Angle *FOD* is an inscribed angle.

_____  **22.** Angle *AOF* is the complement of angle *EOC*.

_____  **23.** If arc *EC* is less than 90 degrees, then angle *AOF* is obtuse.

_____  **24.** Arc *AF* is the same length as arc *BE*.

_____  **25.** The two circles are concentric.

Name _____

**ANGLES:** Calculate the required measures in numbers 26–34 and write the letter of the correct answer in the space at the left.  Answers may be used more than once.  (In circle *O*, arc *AD* = 110°, ∠*COD* = 110°.)

a. 5°        f. 30°        k. 55°        p. 80°        u. 105°
b. 10°       g. 35°        l. 60°        q. 85°        v. 110°
c. 15°       h. 40°        m. 65°        r. 90°        w. 115°
d. 20°       i. 45°        n. 70°        s. 95°        x. 120°
e. 25°       j. 50°        o. 75°        t. 100°       y. 125°

_____ **26.** ∠*BOC*

_____ **27.** ∠*ADB*

_____ **28.** ∠*DAQ*

_____ **29.** ∠*CPD*

_____ **30.** arc *AB*

_____ **31.** arc *CD*

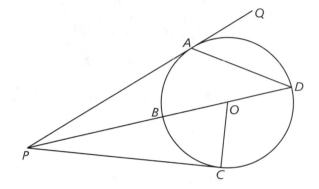

For numbers 32–34 refer to parallelogram *ABCD*.  Each problem is unique.  That is, numbers 33 and 34 have nothing to do with number 32, etc.

_____ **32.** If ∠1 = 30° and ∠2 = 45°, find ∠3.

_____ **33.** If ∠1 = 30° and ∠4 = 40°, find ∠*ADC*

_____ **34.** If *BD* = *AC* and *BD* is perpendicular to *AC*, find ∠2.

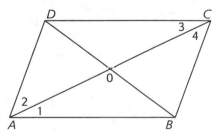

**MULTIPLE CHOICE:** Write the letter of the correct answer.

_____ **35.** The length of a 60° arc of a circle with a radius of 12 inches is __?__ .
        a. 4π in.                    c. 12π in.
        b. 6π in.                    d. none of these

(continued)

_____ **36.** The altitude of an equilateral triangle with a side of 16 inches is __?__ .
     **a.** 8 in.                **c.** 32 in.
     **b.** $8\sqrt{3}$ in.          **d.** none of these

_____ **37.** The area enclosed by an arc of a circle and the chord of the arc is __?__ .
     **a.** a quadrant        **c.** a segment
     **b.** a sector           **d.** none of these

_____ **38.** Two regular octagons have perimeters of 2 in. and 8 in. If the smaller has an area of 16 sq. in., then the larger has an area of __?__ .
     **a.** 4 sq. in.          **c.** 256 sq. in.
     **b.** 64 sq. in.        **d.** none of these

_____ **39.** A square whose area is 144 sq. in. has an apothem of __?__ .
     **a.** 6 in.             **c.** $6\sqrt{3}$ in.
     **b.** $6\sqrt{2}$ in.         **d.** none of these

_____ **40.** The hypotenuse of a right triangle is 10 and one leg is 6. The other leg is __?__ .
     **a.** 6                 **c.** $\sqrt{136}$
     **b.** 8                 **d.** none of these

_____ **41.** The value of $\pi$ can be thought of as __?__ .
     **a.** diameter ÷ circumference        **c.** circumference ÷ diameter
     **b.** diameter · circumference         **d.** none of these

_____ **42.** If a regular hexagon has a side 12 in. long, its area is __?__ .
     **a.** $72\sqrt{3}$ sq. in.        **c.** $432\sqrt{3}$ sq. in.
     **b.** $216\sqrt{3}$ sq. in.     **d.** none of these

_____ **43.** A circle has an area of $64\pi$ sq. in. The area of a square inscribed in the circle is __?__ .
     **a.** $64\sqrt{2}$ sq. in.        **c.** $128\sqrt{2}$ sq. in.
     **b.** 128 sq. in.         **d.** none of these

For numbers 44–48, refer to the figure on the right.     *r* ‖ *s*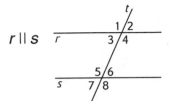

_____ **44.** Angles 1 and 5 are __?__.
       **a.** equal                      **c.** supplementary
       **b.** complementary              **d.** none of these

_____ **45.** Angles 2 and 5 are __?__.
       **a.** equal                      **c.** supplementary
       **b.** complementary              **d.** none of these

_____ **46.** Angles 4 and 8 are __?__.
       **a.** alternate interior angles      **c.** corresponding angles
       **b.** alternate exterior angles     **d.** none of these

_____ **47.** Angles 3 and 6 are __?__.
       **a.** alternate interior angles      **c.** corresponding angles
       **b.** alternate exterior angles     **d.** none of these

_____ **48.** Angles 5 and 8 are __?__.
       **a.** alternate interior angles      **c.** corresponding angles
       **b.** alternate exterior angles     **d.** none of these

_____ **49.** If two sides of a parallelogram are 4 inches and 8 inches in length, and have a 30° angle
       between them, the area of the parallelogram is __?__.
         **a.** 16 sq. in.              **c.** 32 sq. in.
         **b.** $16\sqrt{3}$ in.           **d.** none of these

_____ **50.** The apothem of a regular hexagon that has a 36-inch perimeter is __?__.
         **a.** $2\sqrt{3}$ in.            **c.** $6\sqrt{3}$ in.
         **b.** $3\sqrt{3}$ in.            **d.** none of these